Lie of the Land

Ill fares the land, to hast'ning ills a prey,
Where wealth accumulates, and men decay;
Princes and lords may flourish, or may fade;
A breath can make them, as a breath has made;
But a bold peasantry, their country's pride,
When once destroy'd, can never be supplied,
A time there was, ere England's griefs began,
When every rood of ground maintain'd its man;
For him light labour spread her wholesome store,
Just gave what life requir'd and no more;
His best companions, innocence and health;
And his best riches, ignorance of wealth.

Oliver Goldsmith, 1728–1774

Lie of the Land

Duncan Pickard PhD

First Published in 2004 by the
Land Research Trust
7 Kings Road
Teddington
TW11 0QB, UK

In association with

Shepheard-Walwyn (Publishers) Ltd.
Suite 604, The Chandlery
50 Westminster Bridge Road
London SE1 7QY

British CIP Data
A catalogue record of this book
is available from the British Library

ISBN 0 85683 227 8

Typeset by TW Typsetting, Plymouth, Devon
Printed and Bound in the UK by J.W. Arrowsmith Ltd, Bristol

Cover photograph: the author on his farm in Fife , Scotland

Contents

The Geo-politics of Land & Rent

Ronald Banks

56

Prologue

AS A SON OF THE SOIL, I feel it my duty to unravel the way in which governments misuse the concept of land to deceive taxpayers.

I was born and raised on a livestock farm in east Lancashire and, having passed the 11-plus examination, went to the grammar school in Clitheroe. With brothers who had no aptitude for academic studies, it was made plain from my early teenage years that I should seek employment outside of farming – there being no scope for all of us to work on the family farm.

Having achieved the required "A" levels to gain entry to university, I studied Animal Science and received both BSc and PhD degrees from the University of Nottingham. It was common in the 1960s to study for a year in the United States of America, to obtain a B.T.A. ("Been to America"). In the event two years were spent in postdoctoral research at Cornell University School of Veterinary Medicine and one year at the Mayo Clinic in Minnesota.

On returning from the USA, I accepted a research post at the University of Leeds which led to an appointment as a lecturer in Animal Physiology and Nutrition. My main research interest was the nutritional background to an important disease of dairy cows known as parturient paresis or milk fever. Having married Barbara, a farmer's daughter also from a livestock farm in East Lancashire, we looked for a permanent home in Yorkshire, preferably with some land: we both had ambitions for part-time farming.

In late 1973 an opportunity to buy a 33 acre farm near Ilkley arose and we went to the auction sale with high hopes. The going rate for properties of that type at that time was £1,000 per acre.

A local landowner bought at well above that price and his agent only began to bid when the price was very close to my ceiling. After much negotiation we rented the land with its farmhouse and buildings. The house was barely habitable and we spent, by agreement, the first five years' rent on renovations. It was around this time that my father was heard to describe me to one of his friends as the only one of his sons with enough brains to get out of farming but not enough sense to stay out. In 1974, an adjoining 18 acres of land came available for sale, but because of the crash in property prices the value of the land was £420 per acre. Our high street bank was very reluctant to lend money for land purchase and we had to move our account to another bank in order to acquire the land. Two years later a further 20 acres of adjoining land was offered for sale, but the price had by now risen to £900 per acre. The average price for the two areas was reasonable for the time and this second purchase was made, even though a further move of our bank account was necessary to secure a mortgage.

Having spent any savings, and enlisted the financial help of friends, in-laws and out-laws, we had no money to farm the land and the first few years were spent looking after other people's livestock until sufficient cash was accumulated to obtain animals of our own. Pride in the appearance of the sheep we purchased was never a priority, in fact we gained a reputation for being the buyers of last resort for the poorest waifs in the market. With proper care and treatment and Barbara's diligent attention, we were able to transform some rather forlorn specimens into sheep which others might want to own.

In these early years of farming on our own account, there were many features of rural life which were very difficult to understand. For instance, co-operation between farmers was very rare; some farmers with only a few acres of land appeared to be farming profitably and others with large farms were in serious financial difficulties. We tried to obtain grant aid from the Ministry of Agriculture, Fisheries and Food to replace the very leaky roof on a barn but were told that we did not qualify because we had too few livestock. The fact that we had nowhere to store hay to feed any more animals was irrelevant. This convinced me that subsidised agriculture was designed primarily to aid those who were already well established. Having designed a mineral supplement which was effective in preventing milk fever in dairy cows, sufficient of it was sold to enable us to replace the roof on the barn and increase our livestock numbers. We were then considered eligible to receive subsidies.

Around 1980, I had been introduced to the book *Progress and Poverty* written by Henry George in 1879.[1] His clarity of explanation of economic theory was impressive and many of the anomalies which were evident in the economics of farming became understandable. During the 1980s government financial support for agricultural research, especially research into potential increases in production, was reduced considerably. I opted for part-time lecturing at the University of Leeds and took up consultancy work in the animal feed trade at the same time as increasing our farming activities.

My scholastic interest in farming deepened, however, resulting in the writing of the chapter on the value of agricultural land in *Costing the Earth*.[2]

Our move to Scotland in 1992 followed my resignation from the University of Leeds in 1990 and the sale for housing development of a field which had once belonged to my wife's parents. As we had been farming the land for many years we qualified for Capital Gains Tax roll-over relief on this sale if we further invested in agricultural property. Together with the sale of our assets in Yorkshire (which had increased in price from £25,500 to £185,000 in less than 20 years), we were able to invest everything and borrow some to buy a 600 acre farm in Scotland.

My work with the agricultural chapter of *Costing the Earth* and my reading of *The Power in the Land*[3] convinced me that the peak in land prices would be sometime around 1990, with the following low point likely to be in 1992. These dates were used to guide both the sale of land for building and the purchase of the farm in Scotland. We knew we were selling around a peak in prices and buying at a low point. The cash value of our farm has

[1] Henry George, *Progress and Poverty* (1879); New York: Robert Schalkenbach Foundation, 1979.
[2] Ronald Banks, *Costing the Earth*, London: Shepheard-Walwyn, 1989.
[3] Fred Harrison, *The Power in the Land*, London: Shepheard-Walwyn, 1983.

increased considerably since 1992 and we are often told that we bought a cheap farm. Bearing in mind the fact that the farm's potential to generate profit is no higher than it was in 1992 my response is to say that the farm was the correct price. We based our offer to purchase on the well-established rule of thumb that land is worth 20 times its rental value. It is very likely that we will increase our area of land owned in about 2010, the next low point in land prices.[4] The inevitability of this prediction is made more certain in the light of recent pronouncements from the Scottish Executive and from Dept. for the Environment and Rural Affairs (DEFRA).

The Forward Strategy for Scottish Agriculture contains nothing which will change the general direction of farming in Scotland. The proposed tinkering with the pattern of subsidy allocation towards "Land Management Contracts" will not stop the trend towards larger and fewer farms, with an increasing proportion of the money going to a smaller proportion of farmers and landowners. Rural communities, including schools, post offices and pubs will continue to decline and eventually close.

The CAP subsidy system is to be reformed. Payments will not be linked to production, according to Secretary of State Margaret Beckett in the House of Commons (12 February 2004). Little will change, however: 80% of the money will still go to 20% of farmers. Because we expect subsidies will decline, we plan to farm without them. Like others, we would rather trust our ability as farmers than to live under the stifling bureaucracy associated with becoming "land managers".

Within 25 years of us making a start in farming on a part-time basis on 33 rented acres, there are virtually no opportunities for anyone today to begin as we did. The bottom rungs of the ladder have been taken away. To say that this is the result of progress and of the market in farms and farm land is to ignore the fact that the market, such as it is, is one grossly distorted by an obsolete system of taxation which favours the ownership of property and discriminates strongly against employment. Until there is a radical overhaul, social justice and economic efficiency

---

[4] Fred Harrison, *Boom Bust: Countdown to the Depression of 2010*, London: Shepheard-Walwyn (*forthcoming*).

will never be achieved. It is fraudulent to claim otherwise. My aims are to describe farming as I see it, to try to explain why the policies of the last 50 years have led to the present position, and to propose a remedy.

1

The Big Lie

ON 21ST MAY 2001 I went to the General Election hustings meeting organised by NFU Scotland, in St Andrews. In his address to the meeting the Member of Parliament for Northeast Fife, Menzies Campbell, stated that the average farmer's income in Scotland for this year was £73 per week. I have never been convinced by the published figures for average incomes, which appeared unrealistically low, so following the meeting I sought more information from *Farm Incomes in Scotland 1999/00* published by the Scottish Executive.[1]

This publication describes the incomes of individual farms in terms of average "Net Farm Income" (NFI), which, you may be surprised to know, is not the same thing as the average income of farmers. NFI calculations were introduced following the 1947 Agriculture Act. This introduced a system of guaranteed prices for farm produce with the intention of stimulating production. The system included an annual Price Review at which representatives of the Ministry of Agriculture and of the National Farmers Union met to decide the guaranteed prices for the following year. To guide the negotiations an estimate of farm incomes was needed: if incomes fell, guaranteed prices were increased. It was realised that, because some farms were owner-occupied, others were tenanted, some had only family labour and others only employed staff, an average figure for these various groups would not allow meaningful comparisons to be made. Therefore, quite sensibly, standardisation procedures were used

[1] Scottish Executive, *Farm incomes in Scotland 1999/00*.

Table 1:I	
Taxable Profit for the year	£56,500
Less imputed rent at £60 per acre	£36,000
Less imputed wages for 2 staff	£29,000
Net Farm Income	−£8,500

to calculate NFI. For owner-occupied farms, which had no rent to pay, a figure for rent was imputed, based on the rental value of the farm. Where family labour was employed but no wages were paid, a figure for labour costs was imputed, based on the earnings of similar non-family farm workers.

Despite the fact that there is now a much bigger proportion of owner-occupied farms (about two-thirds) than there was when annual Price Reviews were undertaken (about one-third), and guaranteed prices have been replaced by other ways of subsidising farmers, NFI calculations are still made. *Many farmers who are trading profitably have Net Farm Incomes which are negative.* As an example of the calculations which are made to arrive at Net Farm Income, I have taken a 600 acre farm, which is family-owned and has two family members working full-time in addition to the two parents (*see Table 1:I*).

From a taxable profit of £56,500 to provide a living for four people it is possible to claim that the farm is losing £8,500 per year!

I contacted Menzies Campbell to question the validity of the figure he had given as the average income of farmers. I arranged to see him at his local office. His response was simply to say that the figure of £73 per week had been supplied by the NFU of Scotland and he had assumed that their information was correct. When I explained the basis of calculation of NFI it was obvious that Mr Campbell was unaware of its origins and had been prepared to believe that the average wage of farmers in Scotland was £73 per week.

If Members of Parliament accept figures like these without question, it is not surprising that most other people – including some farmers – also believe what they are told. Even the Prince of Wales, at a press conference at St James' Palace,[2] said that average incomes were £5,200 per farm, and this meant that "a way of life is at risk of collapsing".

I wrote to the civil servant responsible for the publication of income figures for Scotland. He said that NFI should be "viewed as an economic measure rather than as a 'wage' and as such could be 'justifiably used to observe trends over years and between countries'". In other words, average NFI is an *index of income* and is *not* – as the politicians and farm lobbyists present it – the same as the actual earnings from farming.

Why do so many people quote Net Farm Incomes and give the impression that they represent the actual incomes of farmers? Farmers' leaders are content to perpetuate this lie. According to Ben Gill, the President of the National Farmers Union of England and Wales, the average *annual income* of farmers in 2001 was £5,200. This was translated into an average wage of £1.43 per hour, based on a survey by Deloitte Touche which found that farmers' were working an average of 70 hours per week.[3] On 27 July 2001, the president of NFU Cymru, Hugh Richard, was reported as saying that the average *annual wage* for a Welsh farmer before foot and mouth disease was £4,100. The NFU of Scotland's Farming Manifesto published in March 2001 stated that the average *farm income* in 2000/01 was £3,800 or £73 per week, meaning that "Scottish Farming is clearly fighting for its future".[4]

John Kinnaird, the newly elected president of the NFU of Scotland, is content to perpetuate the myth. He said: "The average cereal farmer lost £7,000 in the last financial year, and they can't see any light at the end of the tunnel".[5]

The recently published *A Forward Strategy for Scottish Agri-culture*[6] is obviously based on NFI rather than on actual incomes. How can anyone produce a forward strategy purporting to show the way to sustainable farming which is not based on real farm incomes but on "economic measures"?

---

[2] *Daily Telegraph,* 25 July 2001.
[3] *Farming News,* 5 July 2001.
[4] SNFU Farming manifesto, March 2001.
[5] *Scottish Farmer,* 3 May 2003.
[6] The Scottish Executive Environment and Rural Affairs Department, July 2001.

Even more recently, Deloitte-Touche reported that the national *average profit* for a 500 acre family farm had plummeted to £50 per week.[7]

It is clear from their figures that Deloitte-Touche are content to publish data for Net Farm Incomes and equate them with farm profits. They should know better. In all reports of the perilous state of farm incomes I have seen only one where the figures were doubted. Lord Haskins, in an interview with *The Guardian*,[8] said "That's a distortion, you just have to think for ten seconds, and you say what a lot of rubbish". He did not, however, say why he thought the data were rubbish.

In September 2001 the NFU reported the results of a study of 1,000 tenant farmers, which highlighted the difficulties faced specifically by tenants. Apart from appeals to landowners to reduce rents and relax rules restricting diversification this was another report in the "Oh what a shame" variety. The real reasons why tenant farmers are so much worse off than owner-occupiers were not mentioned[9] (*See Box 1:1*).

By quoting these mythical numbers and pretending that they represent the true incomes of farmers, farmers' leaders must be hoping that government intervention will increase subsidies or guarantee higher produce prices to bring the average NFI up to some "acceptable" figure. Would an average NFI of £20,000 be enough? Even if this could be achieved, tenant farmers would soon be no more profitable than they are now because *those of us who are owner-occupiers would invest the extra money in more land*. This would increase the pressure for rents to rise, and tenants would still end up at the bottom of the income list.

It is difficult to arrive at a figure for the average earnings of farmers because the data are not presented in an appropriate form. But if we start with the average NFI and add to it the amounts which are imputed as a rent, a guesstimate can be made. Taking cereal farmers in Scotland as an example, they had, in 2001, an average NFI of £10,557 and the rents payable are

---

[7] *Farmer's Guardian*, 12 October 2001.
[8] *The Guardian*, 13 August 2001.
[9] *Farmers Guardian*, 28 September 2001.

Box 1:I
How land owners drive up rents

THE FIGURES for average NFI grossly *underestimate* the depth of the plight of tenant farmers.

The view has been expressed that the deduction of imputed rent from the taxable income of owner-occupiers is justified because the remaining "income" is representative of the income from farm production rather than from the ownership of land. The definition of rent as being the surplus remaining after the costs of production for labour and capital have been met, has been converted to mean the money which is due to the owner of land and is the first call on income, with the remainder available to meet the costs of labour and capital. Those familiar with the writings of Adam Smith and David Ricardo would be uncomfortable with this distortion of classical economics, but most modern economists would find it acceptable because they are content to confuse "capital" with "land" and are unable to see the truth.

From the tenant farmer's perspective it is difficult to see how rent could vary as costs of production vary because the rent they pay has rarely if ever fallen and is a major part of their fixed costs. The main reason why farm rents are so high and "fixed" is because the open market rental value of farms and farmland is elevated by the ability of owner-occupiers to pay high prices for additional land. The fact that many owner-occupiers have little or no costs associated with the land they own means that the costs of additional rented land are spread over the whole area they farm. This automatically puts up the rents for tenant farmers who own no land, because farm rents tend to be based on the "open market value", and those who own land can afford to pay the highest rents. The real losers from this inaccurate presentation of farm incomes are the tenant farmers, especially those who rely entirely on hired staff. If they also have substantial bank borrowings for working capital, their financial position is dire.

imputed to be about £150ha, which for the average farm of 124ha would amount to £18,600 per year. Because two thirds of farms in Scotland are either wholly or partly owner-occupied, the average amount to be added to the average cereal farmers' NFI would be £18,600 for owner occupiers. This amounts to an average income of £29,157 per year. By adding the notional rental value of farms to the published figures for average NFI we can see that the average actual farm income is far higher than that which is quoted in the media headlines. This is without accounting for the imputed costs of family labour.

The main purpose of producing average NFI figures appears to be that of providing newspaper headlines. We, as farmers, would never base our business decisions on NFI and none of the advisory services use them as a basis for trying to improve farm profits. Why then would a report sponsored by The Scottish Executive Environment and Rural Affairs Department (SEERAD) describing a forward strategy for Scottish farming, use NFI as their starting point?[10]

---

[10] The Scottish Executive Environment and Rural Affairs Department, July 2001.

2

Exodus & the Price of Land

TO THOSE OUTSIDE AGRICULTURE it is difficult to see that there is any crisis when there are so few farms for sale and so much money waiting to be invested.

Most of the money available for land purchase is thought to be from the sale of development land. However, according to Jim Ward of FPDSavills,[1] there has been a significant influence of money from those with City bonuses, high salaries, good stock market returns and gains from the housing market.

More than a fifth of all farms handled by FPDSavills in 1999, and more than a third of farms with less than 250 acres, went to "new lifestyle landowners". They will pay a lot for a nice house and few scenic acres. Capital gains rollover relief and relief from inheritance tax offer big incentives to invest in farmland. The housing market is having an increasingly important influence on farm prices. According to FPDSavills, "as farm incomes have fallen by 60%, the value of desirable farm houses has risen by 68%". A substantial farmhouse in the correct location can be worth as much as the whole farm was 20 years ago. Since there is usually no liability to capital gains tax on the sale of houses, they are a very attractive investment. As a consequence, a farm with a good house and 200 acres in the right location could be worth £4,000 per acre because the house might make up half or more of the total price.

Given these observations, it would be easy to overlook the fact that when farms are offered for sale, most are bought by other

---

[1] *Financial Times*, 12 November 2000.

farmers. This is especially so when farms are split into several lots (it would be more correct to say they are sold in "bits" rather than in lots). Neighbouring farmers buy one or two fields to add to their own holdings. In this way the total sale price of a farm is usually enhanced, because the farmhouse and a pony paddock would attract a non-farming purchaser and fields sold in ones or twos often make more per acre than when sold in larger lots. It is obvious that not all farmers are in financial difficulties. According to recent evidence, about one-third of farmers in Scotland have no bank borrowings.[2]

Why is land worth in excess of £2,000 per acre to farmers when the prices of grain, meat and milk are so low? A partial answer can be found in the rents offered for land whether for full-time contracts or for summer lets. £100 per acre is commonly paid. Based on the principle that land is worth 20 times its annual rental value, the current price of land is not unrealistic. The figure of £100 per acre rent for good land may be considered rather high, given that the figure used to calculate NFI is about £60 per acre.[3] But I know of land where £100 is paid (especially, as I shall explain in Ch. 3, if the area can be used to claim extra subsidies for extensification).

The clue to rental values comes from the value of subsidies. In Scotland annual payments for cereals and set-aside are about £88 per acre and for protein crops more than £100 per acre. For livestock, depending on the system, subsidies can also reach £100 per acre. In reality, the subsidies pay the rent. It is the landowner who indirectly receives the subsidy, with the farmer making his profit from growing the crops or producing the livestock. If land can be bought at £2,000 per acre and let for £100 per acre per year, a 5% return can be had – plus the prospect of a capital gain.

This arrangement is likely to continue as long as there are ambitious owner-occupier farmers willing to take on extra land in the hope of reducing their fixed costs per acre. If this analysis is correct, it is farm subsidies, capital gains tax roll-over relief, and the favourable treatment of investment in houses which keeps the market price of farmland from falling. Those who

[2] *A Forward Strategy for Scottish Agriculture*, Edinburgh: The Scottish Executive, 2001.
[3] *Farm Incomes in Scotland 1999/2000*, Edinburgh: Scottish Executive Publications.

attempt to predict land prices on the basis of produce prices alone are unlikely to be successful because these other factors are much more important than produce prices when decisions are made to invest in land. By using surplus subsidy income rather than profits generated from the market as the basis for justifying the purchase of more land, farmers are taking a big risk. They should remind themselves that it is politicians who determine the fate of the countryside (*see Box 2:1*). They decide to give subsidies to farmers, and they may also decide to take them away.

According to FPDSavills, investment in farmland compares unfavourably with other forms of investment, because in the last 100 years, in real terms, the gain on land is under 1% per year. This explains why the large institutional investors have sold their entire portfolios of agricultural land. Farmers who already own

---

Box 2:1
Countryside as commodity

THE BLAIR government treats rural life as a plaything for urban politicians. In March 2002 it used Hollywood film stars like Joan Collins to participate in a Leicester Square stunt in the centre of London to "re-brand the countryside".

It seems that hard-working country folk need a multi-million pound marketing scheme to promote rural Britain as "a green and pleasant land". As part of the myth-making, the media did its bit to disparage the productivity of farmers by promoting the misinformation concerning the income they earn. According to the *Sunday Times* (10 March 2002): "Farming . . . generated a net income of £1.7 billion. In England and Wales last year – about a tenth of the value of rural tourism . . ."

This was an example of the abuse of statistics to sell farming as a hard-up, hard-done-by industry that needs to plead for subsidies filched out of the pockets of taxpayers. The income statistics for rural tourism – worth £14 billion a year to the English countryside alone – includes government subsidies to tourism and the rental income extracted by property owners from hotels, pubs and recreational facilities. Similar numbers are excluded from the global sum that purports to be the income of the farming sector.

land have rather different motives for buying more land than institutional investors. Owner-occupiers have the advantage of using the rental income from farming which they do not pay as rent, to ease the burden of repaying any mortgage on additional land.

It is interesting to note that the highest land prices in the United Kingdom are not in the south and east of England, where growing conditions are best, but in Northern Ireland. The reason is that there is no tenanted land in Northern Ireland (apart from short term lets), and almost all land is owner-occupied. When farms are sold they are split so that neighbours have a chance to buy a field or two. The high price of agricultural land is of little benefit to working farmers. For me it would not matter if the price fell to zero. *The high price of land is detrimental to most farmers because it increases fixed costs.* It also makes entry into farming more difficult for young people.

How much longer are we to persist with the perverse notion that high land prices are beneficial to the national economy?

Financial commentators invariably greet rises in the price of consumer goods as being bad and inflationary, but rises in the price of land and other property are described as good. I have never seen a satisfactory explanation for this discrepancy. The most likely explanation may be found in the almost universal belief amongst modern academic and commercial economists that "land" is "capital". This conceptual mistake allows them to believe that increases in house prices can be called "increases in capital formation" which are "good" for the economy. In fact a large and increasing proportion of house prices rises is in the price of the land. There is therefore little or no increase in capital formation when house prices increase because no new land has been formed.

This economic illusion inhibits a correct analysis of the roles of land and rent in the national economy (*see Box 2:II* see page 16). It is, I think, the main reason why most economic forecasts turn out to be wrong. We are led

> A college economist planned
> To live without access to land.
> He would have succeeded,
> But found that he needed,
> Food, shelter and somewhere to stand.
>
> Anon.

Box 2:II
Land Prices & the Business Cycle

THE cycle of land prices occurs in all land, commercial, industrial, domestic and agricultural. The approximately eighteen-year cycle in land prices identified by Fred Harrison* is best described beginning at a low point in the cycle. At this stage those who want to buy land to make a living from working on it can afford to do so. As soon as this "floor" in the market is established, others are encouraged to invest in land and the price rises. Any commodity, such as land, which is in limited supply and which starts to rise in price, generates its own impetus to further rises. Investors see the opportunity to make capital gains from buying and selling land. Speculators drive prices to a level higher than that which those who want to work on the land could afford to pay. Further rises in price continue until it becomes increasingly difficult to find a buyer at a higher price. At this stage those investors (speculators) who are left holding land at the top of the market, especially if they have borrowed to secure their land purchase, try to pay the interest or seek a return on their investment by charging a higher rent to their tenants.

Because tenants cannot, in most cases, afford to pay rents based on speculatively inflated land prices, they quit. Landowners left without income cannot repay their loans and become bankrupt. This leads to enforced sales and the price falls to a level at which those who want to buy land to make a living from it can afford to do so, and the cycle is completed. The cycle is usually characterised by a slow and gradual increase over the first few years followed by a steeper rise which tails off towards the peak; the fall in prices is more rapid than the rise.

It should be noted that external forces can disrupt the shape of the land price cycle. For instance the introduction of Arable Area Aid Payments in 1994 led to a much faster rise in agricultural land prices in the early part of the present cycle than would have been predicted. The housing land market will exercise a major influence on the timing of the next downturn.

*Fred Harrison, *Power in the Land*, London: Shepheard-Walwyn, 1983.

to believe that the "land", "capital" and "labour" theory of classical economists such as Adam Smith is out of date. Modern economists, by ignoring land and rent, are the equivalent of a structural engineer who ignores Newton's laws of gravity because they were discovered a long time ago. The truth is ageless.

High land prices result directly from the favourable treatment of investments in property (which stands on expensive land) for taxation purposes. Capital gains tax roll-over relief is perhaps the best example, but they all make land more expensive than it should be. Conversely, the taxes on employment (Income Tax, NIC and VAT) make labour more expensive. It is not difficult to see why BMW have abandoned Longbridge and that Ford has "downsized" at Dagenham. We see many examples of manufacturing in Britain losing out to cheaper foreign imports. It is not only the reduced labour costs which favour overseas producers but also the lower cost of land. The sooner we realise this, the sooner remedial action can be taken. The alternative is to continue as we are until all manufactured goods and primary agricultural goods are obtained more cheaply from abroad. Unless changes are made, those who think farming is seeing the worst of its financial problems, are suffering from delusion. Our lack of competitiveness was often blamed on the high exchange rate against the euro (the exchange rate against the dollar being conveniently ignored) but we could easily cope with high exchange rates if our fixed costs were lower. Unless our antiquated, complicated and disincentive taxation system is completely overhauled, there is little hope for improvement.

There have been calls for tenant farmers to be allowed to buy their farms, using similar "right to buy" legislation as for council house tenants. This is rejected by landowners who say they would only receive about half the amount their farms would be worth when sold with vacant possession. But the price of a tenanted farm is much closer to that which could be justified by its productive capacity. It would be more valid to argue that landowners are making twice the price their farms are worth when sold freehold.

Allowing tenant farmers to buy their farms would obviously increase the number of people owning land and would be financially beneficial to tenant farmers. However, it would be wrong to believe that the most serious problems of farming would be solved by such a policy, because it would do nothing to improve the chances of newcomers wanting to enter farming, nor would it lower the costs of labour. Large farms would continue to increase in size, perhaps at a faster rate, and rural communities would still decline. Without removal of the tax advantages of land and property ownership there would be great injustice in allowing a tenant to buy at the tenanted price and enabling him then to make a substantial gain by selling at the freehold price.

Those who believe that a substantial tenanted sector is essential for farming are deluding themselves. It is true that the entry to farming for young people used to be through obtaining a tenancy. This is no longer the case. The landlord-tenant system disappeared years ago and has mostly been replaced by the landlord-agent-tenant system. It used to happen that a benevolent landowner would replace an outgoing tenant with the most promising of the sons of an existing tenant or even a newcomer to farming. Nowadays the desire to maximise rental income has removed such sentimental notions and any vacant tenanted farm is likely to be sold or let to the nearest owner-occupier because he can pay the highest rent.

The exodus from farming predicted by the likes of Lord Haskins and Sean Rickard, the former chief economist of the NFU, is being led by farm workers who will be followed by more of their kind and by tenant farmers. Because of their higher fixed costs tenant farmers are the first to shed employed labour. Changes to the Common Agriculture Policy (CAP) which result in reductions in subsidy payments for producing food will worsen the ability of tenants to pay their rent. They will then give up farming altogether. The sequence of events for tenants is already in evidence:

1. Produce prices and subsidy income falls.
2. Employed labour is made redundant.
3. Livestock are sold because their care is relatively labour-intensive and capital is released.
4. Farm machinery is sold and contractors are hired for arable operations.

5. Control over the timeliness of operations is lost and yields fall.
6. Income is insufficient to pay rent and living expenses.
7. The farmer quits.

Although the number of people employed in farming will continue to decline, those who have predicted that the number of farms will halve in the next 20 years are unlikely to see their predictions come true. This is because they fail to take into account the structure of farming in the UK. With about 78% of farms in England and Wales being owner occupied[4] (respective figures for Scotland are about 68% and for Northern Ireland close to 100%), the majority of farmers can afford to stay on their farms and only sell up when they want to do so. The other fact ignored by these forecasters is that almost 40% of holdings in the UK are less than 50 acres and comprise less than 5% of the farmed area of land. The majority of these 93,000 farms are probably farmed part-time and their owners live on farms because they want to. They are relatively unaffected by the pressures that cause full-time tenant farmers so much financial pain.

Another myth that needs to be exposed is the widespread belief that large farms are more efficient than small ones. And we are often told that UK farmers are the most efficient in Europe. These "facts" need to be questioned, because the terms in which efficiency is described are never defined. The only measures of efficiency which support these claims are those of output per farm or per person employed in agriculture. It is therefore obvious that because average farm size is the highest in Europe, UK farms are the most efficient. What about other measures of efficiency such as output per unit area farmed, or per unit of fossil energy used, or per unit of capital employed? Why does no-one compare other indices of efficiency?

Perhaps people like Lord Haskins, who is reported to have said "farms will get bigger and that's a good thing",[5] might not be such staunch advocates of "bigger is better" if they looked at other ways of measuring efficiency.

---

[4] John Nix, *Farm Management Pocketbook 2001*, 31st edn, Imperial College at Wye.
[5] *The Guardian*, 6 August 2001.

Box 2:III
Taxes that kill jobs

TENANT farmers are squeezed out by high rents and by the high costs of employment. Both these factors are the result of existing taxation policies which favour property ownership and discriminate against employment. Many tenant farmers are paying income tax even though their farms are not profitable. Some of them do not realise that they are paying Income Tax. Let me explain this anomaly. On the 19th day of each month every employer is obliged by law to pay to the Inland Revenue money on behalf of his employees which consists of Income Tax and National Insurance contributions (Employer's and Employee's). It matters not to the Inland Revenue whether the farmer paying this money can afford to pay and many see their bank overdraft go up to pay these taxes.

Would it not be more honest to refer to these taxes as Employment Tax because the person who earns the income does not in fact pay the taxes?

For many farmers it is not the take-home pay of farm workers which leads them to shed labour but the 30% to 40% additional money which the Government charges for their employment. It is useless for Government ministers and others in high places to bemoan the fact that 20,000 people have left farming in the two years up to 2002 without seeking to change the major reason for this exodus.

Similarly, those who are content that more jobs will be lost in agriculture in the search for greater efficiency are taking too narrow a view. Sean Rickard is reported as saying "The starting point will have to be acceptance that farming will never create any more jobs; all it will do is shed them".[6] Under the existing tax laws which discriminate against employment, Mr Rickard is correct, but given a more enlightened approach to raising money for public expenditure, his prediction would be wrong. I know from our own farm that the number of people employed is not the result of there being insufficient work to do. In fact there is work for two or three more on the farm, but whereas the

---

[6] *Financial Times*, 6 June 2001.

Government gives tax allowances against depreciation of tractors and other machinery, it penalises us with employment taxes as soon as we employ a farm worker (*see Box 2:III*). By what criteria is this considered to be sensible or rational? Is it little wonder that tractors are becoming bigger and bigger if our profitability is more likely to be enhanced when we buy a new tractor and make a farm worker redundant? Seen in these terms it is difficult to avoid concluding that the inmates are running the asylum.

3

The Stresses of Farming

FARMING HAS BECOME a more lonely occupation. The continuing decline in the number of farms and the even more dramatic reduction in the number of farm workers has heightened the loneliness. The number of suicides in farming is higher than in other occupations, with the remoter rural areas being the worst affected. "The highest suicide rate in Britain occurs in the country's sparsest and arguably most beautiful region, the Scottish Highlands. Its inhabitants are two and a half times more likely to kill themselves than people living in London".[1]

People commit suicide for a large number of reasons. There are documented cases where financial hardship has probably been the main factor, but the statistics of farm suicides are not categorised according to financial status, size of farm, whether the subject was a tenant or an owner–occupier. This means that it is not possible to describe the farming circumstances that would be most likely to induce a farmer to take his own life. High levels of stress, dissatisfaction and working in isolated communities with little social support are thought to be responsible for the excess suicides in farmers.[2] The geographical distribution of suicides in farmers in England and Wales was investigated by Hawton and his colleagues.[3] They suggested that farmers with relatively small holdings experience

---

[1] *The Observer*, 8 May 2001.
[2] S. Kelly, J. Charlton and P. Jenkins, "Suicide deaths in England and Wales, 1982–92: the contribution of occupation and geography", *Population Trends*, London: OPCS, 1995.
[3] K. Hawton, J. Fagg, S. Simkin, L. Harriss, A. Malberg and D. Smith, "The geographical distribution of suicides in farmers in England and Wales", *Soc. Psych. & Psych. Epidem.* 34(3), 1999.

greater stress and may be at more risk of suicide than those with larger holdings. They are also more likely to be farming alone.

From personal experience I am aware that farming is one of the most visible occupations. By that I mean that anyone who knows anything about farming can tell at a glance by looking over a farmer's fields, whether he is doing a good job or not. If a farmer is in difficulties for whatever reason, it is almost impossible to conceal the truth. This means that if a farmer is a failure, he is aware that all his neighbours are aware of his plight. The fact that a farmer is more likely than not to be working alone means that he has no one to help solve his problems and find a way of coping. As I have pointed out in Chapter 2, the burden of taxation on employment means that the most obvious way a farmer in financial difficulties can reduce his costs is by making hired staff redundant. That automatically increases the workload on himself. Hence the increased incidence of farmers working alone.

Perhaps the biggest change in farming over the last 10 years has been the increase in the amount of record keeping required by government officials. Whilst computers have undoubtedly improved our ability to store, retrieve, check and calculate, they have, as a consequence, increased the capacity of government agencies to demand information. This has greatly increased the stress on farmers, especially since an honest mistake in returning information is seldom accepted as such. Masses of data are sent to farmers, with an official disclaimer that if a farmer receives mistaken information it is the farmer's responsibility to find any mistakes and correct them. If a farmer makes a mistake in providing information the immediate assumption is that he is attempting to defraud the agency that requested the information.

The fact that government agencies can renounce responsibility for their errors, and transfer liability onto farmers – who are expected to find and correct them – is not only stressful; it is against the principles of natural justice. It ought to be illegal for the responsibility for mistakes to be passed on in this way, but farmers – while they hold out the begging bowls for subsidies – are unlikely to challenge this injustice.

It has become commonly accepted amongst farmers that officials regard the information relating to farm animals to be more important than the animals themselves. Farmers or, very often, their wives, spend a greater proportion of time looking after records and ear tags, and less time looking after the animals. There is an increasing tendency for farmers to worry more about the next deadline for returning a government form than about the practical operation of their businesses. The deadlines which have to be met for the submission of information cause considerable stress.

- When a cow or a calf dies on a farm, seven days are allowed for the British Cattle Movement Service to be told. When a farmer dies the relevant authorities need to be told within eight days. The rules governing the burial of animals were much more stringent than those covering the burial of farmers.

Do buried animals pose a bigger risk to public health than buried humans? I think not. A farmer whose calf unfortunately died, was, until recently, permitted to bury it, forget it, and get on with looking after the rest of his animals. Now instead of grieving in peace he has to advertise his loss by telling BCMS within seven days and returning the beast's passport.

Every bovine animal has to have a passport, even if it never leaves home. Without a passport the animal is worthless because its origins cannot be traced, and therefore it is deemed to be unfit for human consumption. Each passport resembles a cheque book with many pages to record all changes of residence. Much office space is occupied by passports. Because passports are obviously very valuable, they have to be kept securely and preferably insured. They also need to be available for inspection at short notice by any one of a range of government officials.

Our first hand experience of the stress associated with bureaucratic inspection is illuminating. Two officials from SEERAD spent five days checking all the ear tags of the approximately 500 cattle in our possession. They also checked our records of cattle movements on and off the farm over the previous two years. The officials were quite clear as to how the investigations would be done, but there was no adequate explanation as to why. Regulations dictated from Brussels said what had to be done –

"It is written". We were required to produce evidence that our records were correct when checked against the records held by SEERAD. Only one mistake was found in our records. A calf had been registered as a male which is a female. Numerous mistakes were present in the SEERAD records.

It would be unfair to say we were the only ones suffering from the stress of this investigation. The officials themselves were obviously under stress from the fear of their work being checked by officials from DEFRA or from Brussels. When our one mistake was found, the officials agreed that it was a simple mistake and not a deliberate attempt to defraud. After all, one mistake in the records of 500 cattle could not be described as serious. Nonetheless, the regulations require that we have to pay a fine for this mistake.

Most of the bureaucracy associated with cattle and their movements has arisen since the BSE crisis began in 1986 and reached its peak in 1996, when Stephen Dorrell, the then Minister of State for Health, announced that in the absence of any other plausible explanation, NvCJD was caused by eating beef. Despite much research, there is still no proof that this is true. Other potential causes, such as organo-phosphates, fungal pathogens or trace minerals have not been adequately considered. Since BSE was first reported in 1986 I have studied much of the scientific literature associated with this and similar diseases. The official, government-backed position regarding their origins and transmission, leaves much to be desired.

Will BSE/NvCJD be another of those miscarriages of justice which, on appeal in about 20 years, be found to be a case of imprisoning the most convictable suspect, rather than the real culprit because it was considered expedient by the establishment at the time?

Arable farmers are also not immune to the pressures of red tape. All our crops produced have to meet the requirements of "assurance schemes". This means that we are not only required to grow, harvest and store produce according to specified standards, but have to provide evidence that we have done so. I have no objection at all to meeting the highest standards of production, whether of crops or animals. It is increasingly difficult, however, to accept that the costs of producing evidence for these high standards have to be met entirely at the farmer's expense. It is especially galling that, should the consumers of our produce be able to buy elsewhere at a lower price, they are prepared to do so without requiring the same high standards as are demanded from us, and they resist our demands that labels should show the country of origin. A notorious example was the importation of pig meat in 1999. It was estimated that the increased costs of production as a result of the BSE crisis was about £5.25 per pig but pig meat was imported which was produced under conditions of welfare and nutrition which had been outlawed here. That is why it could be produced more cheaply. *It is disgraceful that the armed services are eating meat from countries other than the UK – some of which cannot claim to be free of foot and mouth disease.* Would the French allow such a travesty to occur?

I have emphasised the effects of isolation and the stress associated with record keeping as factors likely to contribute to suicide, but I cannot exclude the possibility that the generally gloomy picture of farming, which is painted in every farming publication, is likely to aggravate depression. To be repeatedly told that Net Farm Incomes are less than £100 per week and that farming is facing meltdown, would depress even the most optimistic of farmers.

It may come as a relief to know that NFI is a meaningless figure and most of us are earning considerably more than that. The lack of relevance of NFI is also seen from the fact that whenever predictions are made of massive numbers of bankruptcies in farming, they never turn out to be accurate. The financial status of the majority of farmers is nowhere nearly as bad as NFI figures indicate.

The prediction by Lord Haskins that the "number of farms will halve by 2020" is unlikely to come about because the majority of farms are owner-occupied and their owners will stay in business, even if they farm part-time. *The most vulnerable group are the tenant farmers whose financial status is even worse than the average NFI figures indicate.* Unless there is a genuine attempt to understand the fundamental causes of their plight, the future of tenant farming, as we currently understand it, is bleak. Our pessimism about the future is confirmed by the failure of government to resist the political lobbyists who exercise influence on behalf of landowners – an influence which necessarily shapes official thinking about tax policy. The anomalies are dramatised by the way in which the spoils, under the European Union's Common Agricultural Policy (CAP), are shared out. This issue is highlighted by the charity Oxfam, whose report (*Spotlight on Subsidies*) was summarised by *The Times* (22 January 2004) under the headline: "Labour block on reform of CAP benefits rich farmers". Table 3:I identifies the real winners, some of Britain's major landowners who suffer no stress when they are confronted by their bank balances. Farmers owning 2% of the nation's arable land collected 20% of the £1 billion paid in support for cereal crops in 2003. This contrasts with 15,000 smallholders, with 30% of the land, who received 5% of the payout, according to Oxfam. Tony Blair's New Labour government, apparently, has blocked a proposal by the European Commission to cap payouts at £187,500 per farmer, which would have affected just 224 English farmers. It is surely time for the majority of taxpayers and consumers to turn against Europe's agricultural policy, which, as I shall now explain, is based on mad-CAP economics.

Table 3:I
Mad-CAP Economic Winners

	Duke of Westminster	Sir Adrian Swire	Lord Iliffe	Duke of Marlborough	Duke of Bedford	Earl of Leicester	Lord de Ramsey
Wealth*	£4.9bn	£1bn	£150m	–	£370	£70m	–
Arable land (hectares)	1,280	800	1,300	1,600	2,000	981	1,500
Total CAP cereal subsidy (est.)	£366,000	£208,000	£371,800	£568,620	£390,000	£131,000	£382,000

Source: Sunday Times Rich List.

4

The CAP

THE COMMON AGRICULTURAL POLICY (CAP) has had a major influence on agriculture in the UK since Britain joined what was then the European Economic Community (EEC) in 1973.

The original aims of the CAP as laid down in the Treaty of Rome in 1956 were to

- increase productivity,
- ensure a standard of living comparable with that in other industries,
- stabilise markets for produce; and
- ensure adequate supplies at reasonable prices to the consumer.

The relevance of these aims to the European Union of today is questionable, but the need to stimulate the output of farm produce was already redundant 20 years ago. On the contrary, quotas have had to be introduced to limit production.

The average wages of agricultural workers have always lagged behind those of comparable workers in other industries, but official statistics of farm incomes must be treated with extreme caution. Markets for agricultural produce have never been more volatile, especially the prices paid to producers. The fact that there is no shortage of food is not in doubt but whether prices paid by the consumer are reasonable is obviously open to question.

The aims of the CAP have either failed or are no longer relevant. Calls for the reform of the CAP have become more numerous, both from those outside agriculture as well as those within. The failure of the CAP has been inevitable, given that the *real* but undeclared aim was to provide income supplements to the farmers of France, paid for by the manufacturing industries in Germany. *It was a social welfare policy in the guise of an agricultural policy.* It was obvious to many that income supplements based on the amounts of agricultural produce could only lead to surplus production and subsidised export of those surpluses.[1]

In the UK, the first effects of the CAP in the 1970s were seen in cereal farming. Because the guaranteed price (the price at which the Intervention Board of the EEC agreed to purchase cereals) was higher than the market price prevailing prior to joining the EEC, the production of wheat and barley in particular increased considerably. Land was brought into cereal production in more northerly regions and at higher altitudes. That land had previously only been suitable for livestock grazing.

In the livestock sector the Farm and Horticulture Development Scheme had a major impact. It gave capital grants for the "improvement" of farms, up to 37.5% for some projects, for the replacement of farm buildings, land drainage, the purchase of machinery and livestock. In many cases the farmers who took up the offer of capital grants benefited little because they often had to borrow considerable amounts of money to fund the work. Even with the subsidy the investment was not always financially viable.

An out-goers scheme was introduced for milk producers in the name of producing a more efficient industry.

- Because dairy farmers did not have to agree to give up dairying permanently, but only for a minimum of four years, *some were able to receive money for giving up milk production two or three times.*
- During the 1970s some farmers were paid to stop producing milk at the same time as others received grants to establish dairy herds.

The Intervention Board of the EEC, during the 1970s, stockpiled huge amounts of butter and skimmed milk powder at enormous

---

[1] Richard Body, *Farming in the Clouds*, London: Temple Smith, 1984.

cost. The butter was sold at very low prices to Russia and the milk powder made unfit for human consumption by adding copper sulphate. This meant it could only be used in pig rations.

In 1984 milk quotas were introduced as a means of reducing the cost to the EEC of disposing of surplus dairy produce. In the UK those quotas were given to individual farmers. They soon acquired a monetary value because they were effectively licences to produce milk. They could be sold or leased. Huge quantities of quota are traded annually with many quota holders having no dairy cows at all. According to the Intervention Board there are about 30,000 holders of milk quota in the UK of which one in five (about 6,000) do not produce any milk. Rumours have persisted for several years that Manchester United Football Club is one of the largest non-producing quota holders. Having tried to establish the truth of this rumour, I conclude that it is most unlikely, because owners of milk quota also have to own sufficient land to which the quota can be tied.

Farmers who want to start a dairy herd or to expand an existing one have to pay for the quota to do so. In many years the cost of the milk quota needed to sell the milk from a cow has been far higher than the price of the cow itself. The barriers to any young person wanting to farm are formidable, but the entry to dairy farming is virtually impossible.

Particular attention has always been paid to those who farm in the hill and upland areas. Because, to the outsider, nothing much appears to be growing, it is generally assumed that everyone living in these areas is poor and needs financial assistance. The major vehicles for giving money to hill farmers have been the Hill Livestock Compensatory Allowances which, in the words of the Ministry of Agriculture Fisheries and Food, were intended to "Ensure the continuation of livestock farming in the hill and upland areas, thereby helping to maintain a minimum number of people in the less-favoured areas, and conserve the countryside". The effects of the HLCAs have, in many areas, had the opposite effect to these aims.

- It was not unusual for extra payments for cattle and sheep to be given to farmers who were owner-occupiers of large hill farms, even though they had no *need* for supplementary income.

The most effective way for these farmers to keep this surplus income was to use it to buy more land. In that way many of the 80 to 100 acre "starter" farms in hill areas were incorporated into larger farms, depriving would-be farmers of opportunities to farm and reducing the number of people farming in these remote areas. Subsidies have never been allocated according to the recipient's needs. *Why have they never been subjected to a means test, like other social welfare payments?*

More recently the policy makers in Brussels have introduced the concept of set-aside to Europe. Because the costs of storing and exporting surplus cereals was becoming too high, it was considered sensible to limit production by forcing farmers to keep a proportion of their arable land (currently a minimum of 10%) out of production, with an option to put up to 50% of their arable land into set-aside. Payments are made for land which is set-aside at the same rate as for land which is growing cereals. The 10% of arable land which farmers put into set-aside is their least productive land. This means that cereal production is not reduced by the same proportion as the area affected. There is also a tendency to devote more inputs to the area which is cultivated, which also helps to reduce the effect of set-aside.

It is something of a mystery why set-aside was ever introduced in Europe. The United States of America tried set-aside many years ago in a futile attempt to reduce production. This led Joseph Heller in *Catch 22* to describe an American farmer as

> a long-limbed farmer, a God fearing, freedom-loving, law abiding, rugged individualist who held that federal aid to anyone but farmers was creeping socialism ... His speciality was alfalfa, and he made a good thing from every bushel of alfalfa he did not grow. The more alfalfa he did not grow, the more money the Government gave him, and he spent every penny he didn't earn on new land to increase the amount of alfalfa he did not produce ... he invested in land wisely and soon was not growing more alfalfa than any other man in the country.
>
> He was an outspoken champion of economy in Government provided it did not interfere with the sacred duty of the Government to pay farmers

as much as they could get for all the alfalfa they produced that no one else wanted or for not producing any alfalfa at all.[2]

Even more perverse than set-aside for cereals is the concept of "extensification" for livestock. This ostensibly pays farmers to reduce their number of livestock and thereby make farming more "extensive". Anything which implies that livestock farming is intensive is considered to be "bad", therefore extensive farming must be "good". Those of us who keep cattle and sheep below a certain density per unit area are given extra payments per animal for doing so. "Super-extensification" payments are given to those with even fewer animals per unit area. This all sounds fine, in theory. *In practice it means that many farmers in the most unproductive areas are receiving extra payments for doing nothing different from what they were doing before, because the land was unable to support more livestock.* On the other hand, those who farm in more productive areas have a huge incentive to buy or lease sufficient additional land, preferably an unproductive hillside (because it costs less), so that the average stocking density over the whole area falls below the limit which attracts the extra payments.

In most cases the density of livestock on the more productive area has not been reduced and the additional headage payments more than offset the costs of acquiring the additional land. The main effects of the "extensification" policy has been to increase the price of poorer land, whether for sale or rent, increase the rents for existing tenants, and further diminish the chances for anyone who does not already own land, of obtaining any to farm. The catalogue of stupidity emanating from Brussels is endless. I have only listed a few choice examples.

There can be few who would deny that the CAP is in urgent need of reform and many who think that its effects have not been beneficial.

A well respected commentator on farming, Anthony Rosen, wrote: "Farmers today are so brain damaged by subsidies that they cannot see that these harmful government handouts do no more than act as a conduit for higher input costs and higher land prices".[3]

---

[2] Joseph Heller, *Catch 22*, London: Jonathan Cape, 1962.
[3] *Farming News*, 23 August 2001.

Farmers and landowners are reluctant to give up this source of rental income. They hope that the money will still be available through "land management contracts" when it is withdrawn from payments for producing food. The CAP will change to a Common Rural and Agricultural Policy or CRAP. But agriculture is not a popular word with governments and so it will it be dropped, leaving a Common Rural Policy or CRP.

These changes will be made in readiness for expansion of the European Union to include another ten members. Nobody expects the same amount of money per unit area or per head of livestock to be paid to farmers in the newly added countries. The EU budget would not cope, but a CRP would find sufficient to support rural communities by paying for schools, buses and post offices. It is perhaps too much to expect the EU to finally admit that a social welfare policy, rather than an agricultural policy, was intended when the CAP was first started.

On our farm, we are planning to operate in a way that we will be able to survive financially without subsidies within the next five years. I believe that the subsidies available through "land management contracts" will have so many strings attached that they will not be worth the trouble. Like many other such schemes, the major beneficiaries will be those who are paid to administer them.

I fear there will be a rude awakening for those who rely on subsidy income at present rates for the foreseeable future. Many point towards France and say that French farmers will not accept cuts in subsidies, but I believe that under a CRP the smaller farmers in France will still be able to collect brown envelopes for which the more "efficient" large UK farmers will fail to qualify.

A call for an end to the CAP in its present form has come from the Policy Commission on the Future of Farming and Food. Its report recommends that subsidies for agricultural production should be replaced by payments for rural development and protecting the environment. This is yet another document pretending to offer a strategy for the future but which fails to acknowledge the problems to be faced before a sustainable system can be established. It would be helpful if those who aspire to sustainability in farming could explain what they mean by sustainability. According to my dictionary, economic sustainability means prolonged survival without substantial or regular outside financial support. Subsidised farming is, by this definition, not sustainable. Farming will never become sustainable without tax reform to get rid of the burden of high fixed costs.

The European Commission is considering how to de-couple subsidies from production which will inevitably pave the way towards reductions in subsidies. Although the details of the proposals have yet to be agreed it is almost certain that farmers will be able to claim an annual payment based on the amounts they were paid in the years 2000, 2001 and 2002. It is proposed that the money will be paid irrespective of whether a farmer produces anything or not, but he will have to occupy an area of land appropriate to that which attracted subsidy income during the three reference years. There will also be strings attached to the payments, known as "cross-compliance". "Land managers" (it is no longer politically correct to call us farmers) will have to ensure that their land has an attractive appearance and is kept according to regulations. An environmental audit is certain to be required, including a census of the biodiversity of animal and plant life on the land.

Despite the headline grabbing claims that farmers will be paid for doing nothing with their land, I expect that the vast majority of farmers will continue to farm. Most of us are farming profitably and would be financially worse off if we stopped producing crops or livestock. A few owner-occupiers of large holdings without younger family members who want to farm and whose subsidy payments are large enough to support an acceptable lifestyle may be financially able to give up farming. There may be a beneficial spin-off for would-be young farmers to rent land at a reasonable price from non-farming landowners because they could reduce the owner's costs of parkland maintenance.

5

Co-operation & Competition

I N THE SEARCH FOR SOLUTIONS to the problems of farming, co-operation in production and marketing is one of the most frequently quoted routes to financial salvation. Lord Haskins (Prime Minister Tony Blair's rural recovery co-ordinator) has deplored the lack of co-operation between farmers in the UK and compared them unfavourably with those in most continental countries.

The advocates of co-operation fail to appreciate that the lack of co-operation between farmers in Britain is not because they are stupid, stubborn or too independently minded. Co-operation works best where the members of the co-operative are most similar. In Holland or Denmark, for instance, most farms are about the same size and much smaller on average than UK farms. The financial status of the farmers is similar – one farmer is unlikely to have enough money to buy his neighbour's farm. They therefore co-operate as equals in production and marketing.

Contrast this picture with the UK. The most obvious feature of farms here is their dissimilarity, not only in size but in tenure, with large and small farms, tenanted and owner-occupied, within the same locality. Because taxation favours the property owner over the wage earner, personal wealth is increased more securely by maximising the amount of land owned. This means that a large owner-occupier sees his route to increasing wealth, not by co-operating with his smaller neighbour, but by fostering the strategies of predators: waiting for some misfortune (or financial downturn) which might enable the larger to swallow the smaller. It is not in the financial interests of most farmers to co-operate closely with one another.

As Lord Haskins wrote in the *New Statesman* (24 September 2001): "In the past, farmers' co-operatives in Britain have been spectacularly unsuccessful, but there are signs that lessons are being learnt from elsewhere". The first part of this statement is certainly true but I have seen no evidence to support the second. Apart from the obvious financial reasons why farmers do not co-operate, a brief survey of the structure of farmers' co-operatives in this country also reveals why they are unsuccessful.

Whether it is a marketing group to sell lamb or vining peas, or a co-operative to produce and sell animal feed, they follow a similar pattern. Once the initiative for a co-operative is established, a meeting is held at which there is overwhelming support for the obvious benefits of co-operation. The next item on the agenda is usually the election of a board of directors. Invariably those elected are the most successful farmers (usually having the largest farms) in the group. It never seems to occur to anyone to see that the main reasons why these elected directors are such large and successful farmers is because they have single-mindedly expanded their businesses, with no thought whatsoever of co-operating with their neighbours. It is no surprise therefore that the co-operative ethic is not the foundation of the co-operative's trading policies.

Those who are keen to see the development of producers' co-operatives as a way of countering the buying power of the large retailers should be aware of a potential disadvantage. Whilst it may be true that when farmers trade as individuals they can be picked off one at a time, there is a strong possibility that when trading as a co-operative, they can all be picked off at once. I am well aware of the large potential advantages of farmers' co-operatives, but I believe they can have only a small influence on overall profitability without a complete overhaul of taxation.

The most prominent examples of successful co-operation between farmers in recent years can be found in the "machinery rings". These allow machinery and labour to be shared between farms, avoiding the need to have all the machines necessary to do every job on every farm. For instance, we have no machines for spreading the manure on our farm. These are hired in for eight or ten days each year when they are needed. We avoid the capital cost of owning machines that would stand idle for most of the year. Other machines, such as a pasture topper or a combine harvester, we can hire out for use on other farms when we are not using them. Machinery rings only work because the co-operative links between farmers are very loose and all transactions are priced at the going commercial rate. No farmer has to guarantee to provide or receive services through the ring.

Diversification is also seen as a salvation for farming. There is no doubt that the clauses in many tenancy agreements which prohibit commercial activities other than farming, are restricting some farmers' abilities to supplement their incomes. However, not all diversification schemes are successful. Provision, for instance of bed and breakfast accommodation, is popular, but requires considerable capital outlay which is not always easy to recoup. There are very few diversification ventures which do not involve spending money up-front, and on most farms the best way to increase income is to improve the performance of the farm enterprises.

Diversification is unlikely to be a significant feature of British agriculture. To have any chance of success the farm has to be generating sufficient profit to invest in diversification without borrowing a lot of money. If, because the farm is not generating sufficient profit, diversification is necessary, it cannot afford to do so. Catch 22 applies: if you can afford it you don't need to, and if you need to you can't afford it.

The dogma which proclaims that there are too many farmers and that they should "get bigger or get out" to allow those who remain to make a reasonable living, will inevitably reduce the number of people living and working in the countryside. More of the few remaining village schools, shops, pubs and public transport will become unviable.

I have argued that the structure of farming in the UK is a direct consequence of the rules controlling the allocation of subsidies and the collection of taxes. Most of our farming decisions are based on the *economic* consequences of following one path or another. Whilst the rules by which we are governed urge us to maximise personal wealth by maximising the amount of property we own, it is futile to expect us to behave otherwise.

By the same logic there can be no prospect of reducing unemployment when the penalties of employment in the form of income tax and NIC are so severe. If we want to change society for the better we must first of all change the rules under which we are expected to live.

The *Forward Strategy for Scottish Agriculture* published by the Scottish Executive, and the Curry report into the future of food and farming,[1] are typical of almost all proposals for the future, in that there is a lack of breadth of vision. Calls for increased co-operation, diversification, niche marketing, organic farming and the rest are never going to have more than a very small impact on the viability of rural communities. These strategists are like a group of doctors who are so concerned with treating the symptoms of a disease that they ignore its cause. The cure, not surprisingly, is never found.

It is obvious to anyone who cares to look that the agricultural policies of the last 50 years have failed. Despite the massive amount of grant and subsidy money given to farming, we have widespread discontent. Does anyone believe that pouring in even more money will lead to improvement?

Why is there such a lack of idealism? It seems as though our politicians are too concerned with the next election and care too little for the next generation. Is it wrong to want a farming industry where opportunities exist for young people to enter as self-employed farmers or employed farm-workers? Is it inevitable that the opposite scenario prevails, in which farms get progressively bigger and newcomers just cannot get onto the rungs on the farming ladder? Politicians have called for affordable housing for those who live and work in the countryside but they perpetuate a tax system which prevents it from ever happening.

- Fewer and bigger farms will mean that families will be unable to earn a living without working more and more hours and farming more and more land. Is this an attractive prospect?
- Farmers call for less bureaucracy and record keeping but are reluctant to give up their subsidies. Apart from the Farm

---

[1] *Policy Commission on the Future of Farming and Food* (chairman: Sir Donald Curry), 2002.

Assurance schemes, most of the record keeping is for the allocation of subsidies, the Inland Revenue and Customs and Excise.

● Would not life be more attractive if we could do without subsidies in exchange for an end to Income Tax, NIC and VAT?

There is a very real danger farmers will lose most if not all their subsidy income and end up with nothing in return. It would be better to give up subsidies altogether and obtain a massive reduction in bureaucratic control and a fairer and simpler system of public finance.

Farmers often complain that food retailers take far more than their share of the profit margin between the farm and the check-out counter. Some call for a regulator to be appointed, some for prices to be fixed based on the costs of production. Perhaps it would be more sensible for farmers to have a vested interest in the profitability of the retail giants. If abandoning subsidies altogether is not acceptable to the majority, perhaps they should consider converting the £3 billion a year paid in subsidies into non-transferable supermarket shares. In this way, they would receive annual dividends from the profits made because supermarkets pay farmers too little for their produce. But even if this happened, without tax reform the dividend income would end up supporting high rents and land prices.

All kinds of clubs and societies based in rural areas are struggling for members, including the Young Farmers Clubs, Farmers Discussion groups, the Women's Institutes and even the Farmers Unions. The present strategies for agriculture point to continuing decline for all of them yet none has a sensible proposal for radical change. I use the word *radical* in its true sense, which relates to the *root* of the problem, not the popular distortion, which implies superficial left-wing socialism.

The main reason why we lack the urge to examine the causes of problems in society in general and in agriculture in particular is that those who would benefit from radical change lack the ability to effect change. Those young people who have the ability to change things are too busy making a living and paying for a house to get involved. Those who would be able and are in a position to effect change are too comfortable with the status quo, or have been put where they are by those whose privileged position might be threatened by radical change.

The root cause of most of our problems is not the absence of co-operation. It is the antiquated, complicated and disincentive system of taxation under which we labour. It would be difficult to devise a worse way to pay for the necessary functions of the state. Ronald Banks has estimated that the disincentive effect or "deadweight loss" of current taxes costs more than £14,500 per year per head of population.[2] He makes a convincing case for anyone drawing up a budget for public spending to include a third column which would show the true cost of the various taxes.

The radical solution is traditionally called Land Value Taxation. The revenue from public charges on the market-based rent of land would be *substituted* for income tax, NIC, VAT and corporation tax. These taxes impose enormous disincentive effects on economic activity, especially on employment. The introduction of public charges on land rents would be a major boost for the economy. It is often said that a successful national economy depends on a successful agriculture but the converse is also true: successful agriculture depends on a successful national economy.

Land rent charges would be levied on all land, urban and rural, including disused land in towns and cities, on which no tax is currently paid. Valuation would be based on the value of the land alone and would exempt the undepreciated value of improvements such as houses, buildings, fences or growing crops. Any restrictions on the use of land would be taken into consideration, such as green belts or urban parks, when valuations are made – which is what already happens, in the market, when people buy land.

Although rural land accounts for about 87% of Britain's total land area, it represents only about 5% of the total land value. It therefore follows that 95% of the tax burden would fall on those

---

[2] Ronald Banks, *Double-cross*, London: Centre for Land Policy Studies, 2001.

urban areas best able to pay it. The poorest land which has no rental value would not be liable to pay a charge on non-existent rents. Land only has value if it is capable of yielding some financial reward to those who occupy it. So those who think that a land value tax would bankrupt farmers on the poorest land have not understood the nature of this proposal.

A consequence of introducing public charges on land rents – if they were high enough – would be that speculative investment in land would cease to be profitable. The trading price of land would fall. Land in urban areas which is currently disused, but suitable for development, would be developed, thereby reducing the cost of building land and house prices. The planning system is often blamed for the shortage of development land and high house prices, but the ability of speculators to hold land out of use, restricting its supply in the hope of future rises in price, is aided and abetted by the tax system which encourages them to do so.

Without employment taxes, labour costs would fall and financially endangered farmers would enjoy an improvement in their economic circumstances. The move towards organic farming is seriously handicapped by the present taxes on employment. Because organic farming is necessarily more labour intensive than the conventional kind, it cannot compete.

To farmers who fear a fall in land prices, I pose the question: "Who benefits from high land prices?" The answers are clear enough.

- People who want to trade in land
- Bankers who feel more comfortable when the value of collateral is high.
- Land agents selling on commission.

What do those who want to enter farming think of high land prices? It matters little to me whether my farm is valued freehold at £1m or £1,000. The *earning capacity* of the farm should matter rather than its *collateral value* in deciding whether a farmer can afford to borrow money.

Bankers, too, should be more concerned with the ability of borrowers to repay than with the value of assets available in bankruptcy proceedings following their bad lending decisions. There may be signs that this is happening already if comments by Jim McLean of the Royal Bank of Scotland are a reliable guide. He is quoted as saying: "If land values dropped it would not stop us lending but we would be looking for strength in the business".[3] This is a welcome approach and a sign that those with sound plans and the willingness to work hard might have as good a chance to borrow as those who are collateral-rich.

Under the present taxation system, which favours the ownership of land and discriminates against employment, farmers are encouraged to maximise the area of land they own. Public charges on the rent of land would encourage farmers to minimise the area they farm to the most profitable size suitable for them. The outlying fields which cost most to farm would be disposed of to someone who could use them more profitably – such as a young person wanting to make a start in farming. The urge to maximise the area farmed contributed directly to aggravate the outbreak of foot and mouth disease (FMD). Many of the farmers whose animals were lost through FMD had livestock on fields away from their main holding, and it is obvious that the risk of spreading disease is much greater where farmers do not have "all their land at home". Present policies will inevitably lead to ever more farmers travelling longer distances to attend to their stock.

It is widely acknowledged by farmers that land of equal fertility which is farmed at a distance from the main holding is much less profitable than that on the main holding. One of the reasons why we decided to move to Scotland was that in England we had livestock on land in four different locations and spent (wasted) considerable amounts of time and fuel looking after them. Apart from this, we were not doing a very good job of farming those animals because it was impossible to see *all* the animals sufficiently early in the day to minimise the problems which all livestock are likely to present during the grazing season.

Fiscal reform is not offered as the solution to all the problems facing farming and rural communities, but without it I believe that most of the problems will never be solved. Those who dislike my remedy need to answer this question: "What are the prospects

---

[3] *Farmers Guardian*, 29 December 2001.

for farming under the existing tax system?" More of the same
does not look promising to me.

I am sometimes asked "Would public charges on rent raise
enough revenue to pay for Government expenditure?" The answer
is "Yes". *All current taxation is at the expense of rent.* Market rents
are net of people's tax liabilities. This means that if there were no
taxes, rents would increase to absorb the surplus currently
appropriated by taxes. An example of this was seen when
agricultural land was de-rated in the early 1930s. Many tenant
farmers had their rents increased to offset the removal of the
liability to pay rates. The same was seen when urban enterprise
zones were created in the 1980s. When exemption from rates was
allowed, rents and land prices increased accordingly. Revenue from
the rental value of all land would be sufficient to cover existing
taxes on labour and capital. Moreover, if the costs of employment
were reduced by the abolition of employment taxes, more people
would find work. The major cost to the social security budget
would be reduced and the total fiscal needs of the state reduced.

To those who think the abolition of Income Tax is mere
fantasy, I can point to the fact that Britain came within an ace
of seeing such a fantasy become reality. Winston Churchill in
1907 piloted a Bill through parliament which would have
scrapped Income Tax and levied the whole budget by the taxation
of ground rents in urban areas. The landowners in the House of
Lords vetoed the Bill. It is widely known that the House of Lords
lost its right to veto Finance Bills from the Commons in 1911,
but very few are aware that the issue over which that right was
lost was the immensely popular demand to switch taxation from
people's wages and savings on to land values.

The longer reform is delayed, the more difficult it will become
when tax reform is forced upon us. The increasing mobility of
trade as a result of improvements in information technology is
already making the collection of taxes from multinational
companies more difficult. Demographic changes will mean that
income tax and VAT will be unable to pay for public spending.
Manufacturing industries are in decline in this country because
costs of production are lower elsewhere. The present tax base is
becoming increasingly unviable.

Despite the best efforts of institutions such as the IMF and the World Bank to persuade former communist countries that our systems of taxation and public spending are the ideal to be emulated, some, including Russia, are not so easily convinced and are seriously examining resource rents as the alternative source of public revenue. If they adopt this policy and release the potential of their natural resources and human initiative, the financial viability of western economies, saddled with huge fixed costs of production, will be further threatened.

The Scottish Executive is studying the feasibility of moving to a land value-based revenue system in the longer term. I presented oral evidence in its favour to the Local Government Committee on 11 December 2001. Initially, land rent charges could replace the Council Tax and Business Rates. NFU Scotland is also not unfamiliar with the principles of public charges on the rental income of land. It may come as a surprise to some farmers to learn that their membership subscriptions are calculated according to the value of the land they farm. Land in capability class 1 attracts a membership fee twice that in capability class 5.

More politicians have been made aware of the virtues of land as a revenue base since the publication of Don Riley's *Taken for a Ride*, which offers an excellent description of the way public expenditure on transport makes wealthy landowners richer still.[4] Is it too much to hope that those who are concerned with agriculture and the countryside will begin a sensible debate about radical change instead of pinning their hopes of significant progress on tinkering with existing discredited policies?

---

[4] Don Riley, *Taken for a Ride*, London: Centre for Land Policy Studies, 2001.

6

Bright Potential & Gloomy Prospect

BRUSSELS HAS INDICATED that expansion of the EU in 2004, to take in another 10 countries, means that new members' farmers will receive 25% of the subsidy income per hectare of those in existing member countries. This percentage will increase to 100% by 2013. Since the total budget available to subsidise farmers will not increase it is inevitable that the subsidy income of UK farmers will decline markedly from 2004.

Unless there is a dramatic reduction in costs of production many farmers will be unable to stay in business. Tenant farmers are particularly vulnerable. Their holdings will be farmed by ambitious owner-occupiers – those who usually do not need to expand but are usually the only ones who can afford to do so. If the major costs of production – land and labour – could be reduced by enlightened tax reform, the trend towards fewer and bigger farms could be halted and even reversed.

The most important effect of fiscal reform would be on employment. The cost to UK farmers of the current system of taxation based on income tax and NIC is about £2 billion per year. I have calculated this figure from the estimated cost of administering and paying these taxes for the approximately 100,000 full-time employees having an average gross wage of £14,500, and their employers an average tax bill of £4,000 per annum for each. This amounts to £400m per year.

In addition I have estimated that it costs each farm holding at least £2,000 per year to administer these taxes and VAT. The total cost for 240,000 holdings is £480m per year. Because the tax system is so complicated, most businesses have to employ an accountant, and I think the least any farmer would expect to pay would be £2,000 per year, adding another £480m per year to the costs of farming.

The average council tax bill for farm houses is probably in excess of £1,000 per year (ours is £1,450), making an additional cost to farming of £250-300m.

With the costs of taxation of part-time, casual and seasonal workers and the income tax and NIC contributions of self-employed farmers, their spouses and partners, it is easy to see that the present drain of taxation on farm incomes is in the region of £2 billion every year.

The annual total costs of taxation to farmers is of the same order of magnitude as the amounts of subsidy paid or the total Net Farm Income, but the effective burden of taxation on farming – the losses imposed because of the way in which government raises revenue (rather than *how much* it raises) – is crippling. Would it not be more sensible to try to stem this flow by advocating tax reform than to persist in pleading for increases in subsidies?

Paying fees to accountants for minimising our tax liabilities has never seemed to be a satisfactory arrangement. I would rather they were employed to maximise profits than to minimise tax. It is such a waste of the talents of these diligent and intelligent people to be looking backwards over accounts of what has happened rather than helping to look forwards and plan ways to improve profitability.

I have recommended the reform of taxation as the primary solution. Because the rental charge would be levied on all land, the financial advantages of owner-occupiers over tenant farmers would greatly diminish. The public levy on land rents charged to landowners cannot be passed on to tenants. The price of both land and rent would fall and landowners would sell any land they could not farm profitably themselves. This would reduce the price of entry into farming, thereby improving the chances of attracting young blood into the industry. Those who farm the land would own it and those who own the land would farm it.

The removal of grants and subsidies need not have a negative impact on the profitability of farming. Without the burden of existing taxes, farmers would be able to return to farming and concentrate on producing the goods that consumers want. Those who are convinced that unsubsidised farming can never be profitable can take comfort from the fact that if farmers are unable to generate profit (which means the land they occupy would not attract rental charges), there would be no payment to the Exchequer. But when fixed costs have been reduced, there is little doubt that a taxable surplus will be produced. Those markets for primary produce in which we now have difficulty competing, such as dairy produce from New Zealand, would become more open to us. Instead of farming to maximise subsidy income we would pay more attention to the demands of the market. When incentives to maximise the amount of land owned is replaced by incentives to maximise profits through the ability to keep what we earn, the vitality of rural communities will return.

That's what I hope. What do I really expect the near future of our farming communities to be? The clues are to be found in documents like the *Forward Strategy for cottish Agriculture*, which contains nothing which will change the general direction of farming. They are also contained in agricultural policies pursued by governments of the rich nations, such as the USA (*see Box 6:1*).

Box 6:I
A double windfall

US PRESIDENT George W. Bush added fire to world food markets with his $150 billion subsidy plan – and in doing so, has added further fuel to the fire raging in the agricultural land market.

According to *The Christian Science Monitor* (January 4, 2002), under the heading "Farm subsidies prop up Midwest land values", farmland prices were rising to levels not seen in 20 years. And, added reporter Laurent Belsie, crop land prices could soar even higher.

"The reason: government subsidies are propping up real estate values. This distortion helps farmers who own all or most of their land. But it makes it tougher for young farmers and others who rent most of theirs. And it's proving a taxpayer-supported windfall for non farmers who own agricultural real estate.

"Such rising values look out of whack while crop prices are falling. In Illinois, the average agricultural acre costs 18% more than it did in 1981 even though the price of its major crops, corn and soy beans, fell by a third.

"Federal supports for eight major crops have pushed land prices above their natural levels".

According to a recent US Department of Agriculture report, American farmers own slightly fewer than two in every five acres on which they grow subsidised crops. "That means operators who own all their land get a double windfall: all the direct subsidies and the indirect rise in land values," reported Belsie. She added:

"But those who rent land, especially younger farmers just getting started, don't benefit from its rising value. In fact, they pay for it in the form of higher rent payments to landowners. Sometimes, depending on how their lease is structured, part of their federal subsidies flow directly to the landowner".

Epilogue:
Lessons from Russia

THE INVITATION TO TESTIFY to the Agrarian Committee of the Russian Parliament, the State Duma, on their proposals to privatise land, was an experience which, for me, invited reflections on western farm policies as well as to offer a critique of Soviet doctrines.

The first point that had to be established was that the most valuable land in Russia was in commercial, industrial and domestic occupation – just as it is in other countries. To be frank, the Agrarian Committee – which at that time (May 1996) consisted of the directors of the collective farms – was not the most appropriate forum to decide on the future of land ownership. It was understandable that the Russian people would see the word "land" as applying to land which is in agriculture – such a notion is not uncommon in Britain.

The second major difficulty was to convince Russia's parliamentarians that land has commercial value. As a result of the Marxist ideology, which taught that land has no value and that all value is created by labour, it was not easy for them to accept the notion that land could be bought and sold for money. To this day, it remains difficult for Russians to accept that people can own land: their instinctive feeling is that people belong to the land. They believe in the concept of the land being their mother.

By the end of the tour in Moscow, my host, Dr Vyachislav Zvolinsky, a Deputy in the State Duma, was convinced that land had value. To drive this home I offered to buy the collective farm of which he is director. He was aware of the fact that the prices offered by Westerners for property in Russia were only about 1% of the prices paid for similar property in Western Europe.

The recommendation our delegation made was that the land of Russia should not be sold, but should be leased by those who wanted sole rights of occupation. The land should be leased to the highest bidder for an agreed length of time. The money received by the state would fund the necessary functions of the state (defence, law and order, etc.), which would enable it to abolish the cumbersome and disincentive taxes on income and production such as we in "progressive" countries have to suffer.

Dr Zvolinsky invited me to visit his collective farm in southern Russia, between Volgograd and the Caspian Sea. It was decided that some knowledge of the Russian language would be helpful before accepting this invitation. It was whilst studying Russian at night school in St Andrews that my wife, Barbara, and I were introduced to a charity which helps the people of Belarus to cope with the radiation damage caused by the Chernobyl disaster. Two children from the Minsk region stayed on our farm in Scotland for a month around Christmas 1996, and their families had repeatedly asked us to visit them. In 1998 we decided to make a combined trip to Belarus and to Russia.

Our hosts in Belarus live about 100 miles from Minsk in a village that was one of three forming a collective farm of 40,000 hectares. Approximately 1,000 people worked on the farm, a similar workforce per unit area to that which prevailed in Scotland 40 to 50 years ago.

All the people in the villages – even the school teachers – had their own plot of land, mostly from 600 to 1,000 square metres, on which they grew potatoes, tomatoes, cucumbers, beetroots and other fruit and vegetables. Most kept a cow, pigs and chickens. The "private" cows grazed designated areas during the day. Hay was also made for winter feed, from roadside verges and from open land. Each domestic plot was very well fenced and was very productive: a lot of time was diligently devoted to its cultivation.

The contrast between these plots and the collective farm was startling. No fences existed between fields and the collective farm

cows had to be tended by two or three people to stop them from
wandering into the areas of wheat, barley or rye or from being
lost in the forests. The lack of fences prevented effective
management of the grassland, which was generally full of weeds.
The cows had to be kept indoors at night, which probably
contributed to the low level of milk production. Despite three
times per day milking, average yields were only 15 litres per day,
less than half the yields of cows in Britain.

The farm machinery was old – no money has been available in
recent years to buy anything new. With such a large workforce it
was not surprising that many tasks were performed manually and
the farm's 40 horses were kept busy, but a lot of the work did
not appear to be very productive.

Though the people in the villages were poor by our standards
and many were affected by Chernobyl radiation, they appeared
to be fit and healthy. Few had flush toilets and some had no
running water in their houses, but their home-produced food was
good. Many aspects of their life were enviable – small children
could roam freely for hours without parental anxiety, the degree
of neighbourly co-operation, including barter, was high, everyone
had free access to forests for mushrooms and berries and to rivers
and lakes for fishing.

The decline in the value of wages in recent years was the most
common cause for complaint, as a result of the massive increase
in the price of fuel which has to be imported from Russia. The
people were, however, unforgettably generous and hospitable –
their parties consisted of masses of food, innumerable toasts and
abundant quantities of vodka and laughter.

Soon after arrival in the Southern Russian village where Dr
Zvolinsky lived it was obvious that there were similarities in the
social and economic conditions to those prevailing in Belarus.
Here also there were marked contrasts between the privately
cultivated plots of land and the collective farms, although Dr
Zvolinsky's collective farm had obviously been, in previous years,
one of the most productive. Its irrigated land produced rice,
tomatoes and water melons. Such had been the output from the
collective farm that wage bonuses had been paid, television sets
and cars became common and there had been migration into the
area. The research institute located on the farm had been

earmarked for expansion, with a start made on the construction of new houses for the expected increase in staff.

The "new" houses now stand derelict. Since 1991 everything has been in decline. The output of cereals in 1998 was down from 7,000 tonnes to 700 tonnes. Fuel prices had increased one thousandfold in recent years and the fuel for irrigation pumps could not be afforded. Not a single tractor on the farm had a battery and they all had to be parked on slopes so that they could be bump-started.

The villagers were very busy looking after their plots and gathering hay from the common land alongside the Volga river. It was obvious that the importance of the produce from their own plots had increased considerably as the value of their earnings from paid employment had declined. Concern was expressed that the televisions which had so easily been afforded 10 years ago would not be replaced when they broke down.

If what happened on Dr Zvolinsky's collective farm was typical, it is not difficult to believe that total agricultural production in Russia has declined by at least 30% since 1992. The command system of organising agriculture was far from perfect but total neglect is much worse. The effects of such a massive rise in fuel prices in such a short time would have crippled any farm that depended on mechanisation. Our own farm would soon look very different if fuel suddenly became 1,000 times dearer.

Our short stays in Moscow and St Petersburg were sufficient to show us that it was more difficult for those without well-paid employment to avoid total poverty in the cities than in the rural villages. We were told, however, that about 80% of families in Moscow had access to a dacha, which was a piece of land, 600 square metres, previously known as a "collective garden" which was given for the purpose of growing the family's food. Early regulations governed what had to be grown, but since 1991 all rules have lapsed. We visited a dacha outside St Petersburg and saw the enterprise and initiative that was capable of turning quite poor land into the means of producing all the fruit and vegetables for a family of four. Every weekend in the summer was spent on the dacha and it was evident that the dacha system was the Russian form of social security. Given access to land, the willingness to work hard and the ability to keep all the products of their labour, the people could not only avoid starvation but could, in fact, eat rather well.

We left for home with feelings of high regard for the people we had met, whose capacity to make the most of very difficult conditions was admirable. It is regrettable that the old order was destroyed without a plan for anything better. This has led to a few becoming very rich indeed by plundering the natural wealth that should be available to improve the lives of the people. One Russian told us: "At least the previous rulers appeared to care for the country and the people – those in the present government care only for themselves".

The economic potential of Russia is enormous. Should it succeed in establishing a market economy with a tax system that avoids penalising those who work, it will be a competitive challenge for any country in the world.

Since my visit to Russia, I have discussed the advice our delegation gave to the State Duma. This was to fund the necessary state functions from the lease of land and natural resources. Everyone, including fellow farmers, agreed that our proposals made good sense and would be much better than the system operating in Britain. These same people, however, were equally convinced that designating land values as the fiscal base could never operate successfully here.

What of the future in Russia? Even if President Putin decided next week to follow our recommendations it would be many years before economic output would be sufficient to eliminate poverty. There is a powerful minority who have gained sufficient financial power since 1991 that they will not easily be persuaded to allow people a more equitable share of the natural wealth of Russia.

The International Monetary Fund (IMF) is also opposed to adopting a fair system of public finance – it wants to lend more money at high rates of interest and is against anyone who says the Russians do not need to borrow money. Our proposals were condemned by the IMF as not being "capitalist", to which we reply: "No capitalist sells when he can make sufficient money by leasing!"

President Putin is on record as favouring a system of taxation based on natural resource rents. There are increasing numbers of academic economists who are supportive too. The outcome in Russia will depend on the struggle between the few oligarchs, who are now in control of nature's resources and who want to become even richer, and those who want everyone to benefit from the enormous potential wealth of the country.

The Geo-politics of Land & Rent

Ronald Banks

DUNCAN PICKARD'S *exposé* needs to be located in the politics of globalisation, for the lessons are relevant for consumers and taxpayers throughout the rich nations and the developing world. Dr Pickard's narrative traces the way in which Britain's taxpayers are hoodwinked into parting with money ostensibly to help farmers who are supposed to be struggling on the breadline. Breadline? That's what you would think if you believed the official statistics. They are designed to deceive. But the issues range far beyond the problem of producing our daily bread. I shall identify some of the themes which need to be reassessed in the light of the evidence of statistical manipulation by public agencies.

Take, for example, the notion of poverty. Nature, according to the doctrine inherited from the 19th century, is niggardly. Economists observed the widespread malnourishment among the labouring classes in the early decades of the Industrial Revolution, in both the urban centres and the countryside. Influential social commentators like the Rev. Thomas Malthus placed responsibility on the shoulders of the poor people. The ruling classes were exonerated.

Today, the Food and Agricultural Organisation estimates that the number of under-nourished people in the world increased by 18m people in the second half of the 1990s. This brought the total in 2001 to 842m people.

Is nature niggardly? Are the poor the architects of their fate? We have the scientific and technological capacity to produce as much food as we need to feed everyone. The riches of nature, when combined with the ingenuity of the tillers of the soil, fulfil our biological needs. The explanation for the tragedy of poverty and hunger must be found in the laws of men rather than the laws of nature.

In his study of the British and European agricultural systems, Dr Pickard stresses that the problem is to be found in the financial arrangements surrounding the way we use and abuse land. The politics of food is not just about how much meat and potatoes we can place on people's plates. We are dealing with problems which, at first sight, appear far removed from the laws that regulate the production of food. But, in fact, those problems are the collateral damage of perverse systems of land tenure and taxation. An example – terrorism – is engaging much of the time of elected leaders today, so it may warrant examination from a fresh perspective.

The geo-political crisis that is portrayed as the "clash of civilisations" is explained by President George Bush in simplistic terms. He ascribes the need for the US doctrine of pre-emptive strikes and regime change to the hatred that malcontents allegedly have for the freedoms which are championed in the United States. One major embarrassment for the supporting explanation for the US doctrine is that *it fails to account for the home-grown terrorism within the USA*. Understanding the origins of that domestic terrorism may shed light on why some people in the Islamic world also feel frustrated and resort to the use of violence. (Understanding the causes of violence, of course, is not an implicit acceptance of the acts of violence.)

In the past 40 years, an extensive movement has developed in the US which takes the form of a right-wing hostility towards the federal government. This was nurtured by attitudes which, according to author Gore Vidal, have their "deepest root in those dispossessed of their farmland in the last generation".[1] The documentary evidence for the corporate lobbying that led to the displacement of people from family-scale farms was provided by

---

[1] Gore Vidal, *The Last Empire*, London: Abacus, 2002, p.197.

a Colorado journalist, Joel Dyer.[2] He has uncovered the blueprint for getting rid of the nation's small farmers. In 1962, corporate executives gathered to develop a programme for the "consolidation" of farmland into larger units (called *An Adaptive Program for Agriculture*). The strategies it defined were employed by the US Federal Government to cleanse rural America of its yeoman land-tillers. Gore Vidal summarised the outcome:

> So a conspiracy has been set in motion to replace the Jeffersonian ideal of a nation whose backbone was the independent farm family with a series of agribusiness monopolies where, Dyer writes, 'only five to eight multinational companies have, for all intents and purposes, been the sole purchasers and transporters not only of the American grain supply but that of the entire world.' By 1982 'these companies controlled 96% of US wheat exports, [and] 95% of US corn exports'.[3]

The separation of people from family farms has resulted in several forms of alienation. The best-documented process is the migration of landless labourers to the cities where they dwell in slums and eek out an unhappy existence on the margins of the industrial economy. In the UK, in the 18th century, the highland clearances and lowland enclosures provided the proletariat for the urban factories of the Industrial Revolution. In the US, in the 19th century, the emancipation of the slaves performed the same service for the great industrial centres of the North. In the 20th century, thanks in part to the support from the Welfare State, it was possible for some of the displaced people to try and opt out of society: they formed communes which usually coalesced around charismatic figures. A number of these experiments in separate living were terminated by multiple deaths which Gore Vidal characterises as massacres perpetrated by the FBI.

Joel Dyer's narrative suggests a conspiracy theory to dispossess the small farm owners of America by the big corporations. Conspiracy theories, by their nature, are hard to prove; so the explanations offered to account for pathological official behav-

---

[2] Joel Dyer, *Harvest of Rage: Why Oklahoma City is Only the Beginning*, Boulder: Westview Press, 1998.
[3] *Ibid.*, p.199.

iour is easily dismissed by spokesmen for the organs of the state. But the ease with which a government might conspire against its citizens, when it comes to manipulating the distribution of rental income from the resources of nature, is now being documented in the case of the Bush Administration's determination to invade Iraq.

According to Paul O'Neill, who was President Bush's Treasury Secretary for two years, the intention to invade Saddam Hussein's domain to carve up the oil resources was declared in January 2001. Long before terrorists from the Middle East had crashed airliners into the Twin Towers of New York, George W. Bush had declared that he wanted an excuse to take over Iraq. O'Neill's disclosures appear in his memoirs.[4] He supplied documentary evidence that proved the intention to find an excuse for an invasion so that the petroleum reserves could be carved up by the multi-national oil companies. Tony Blair fell for the story that Saddam Hussein was developing weapons of mass destruction, and dragged an unwilling Britain into the American imperial project to provide Bush with the semblance of international support for what was, in fact, a dirty little private war engineered by a clique of Washington neo-conservatives. The rent of oil was the spoils of war. It remains to be seen whether the US Government really will abide by its public statements, that the oil of Iraq belongs to the people of that nation. The answer will have to be found in the way in which Iraq disposes of the rental income of petroleum: will this be mortgaged to, and appropriated by, western financial institutions?

Land reform does not feature in the high level negotiations between nations; the land problem *is* the single most challenging issue before the world's statesmen and diplomats. For example, it underlay the dispute that led to the breakdown of the World Trade Organisation (WTO) conference in Mexico in September 2003. That event saw the emergence of a block of 20 nations (G20) which served an ultimatum on the richest (G7) nations. The provocation for the conflict was the agricultural policies of the G7, which subsidise their "farmers". But the terms in which

---

[4] Ron Suskind, *The Price of Loyalty: George W. Bush, The White House and the Education of Paul O'Neill*, New York: Simon & Schuster, 2004.

agricultural policy is discussed conceal the reality. Subsidies of $300 billion every year are ostensibly granted to aid production, but in fact they do not raise the entrepreneurial rewards of working farmers or the wages of their labourers. They are capitalised into higher land prices. In other words, the protectionism that distorts world markets for cotton, rice and wheat drives up the price of land in North America, Europe and Japan. This outcome is the logical result of the history of perverse refinements to land tenure and public finance in the G7 countries.

Farmers in the developing world are excluded from the food markets of the rich nations by an ethic which serves the exclusive interests of landowners and agri-corporations. The wage earners in the G7 countries are forced to pay higher taxes and prices for food.

Perverse land and tax policies will loom large within Europe over the next few years. The European Union will struggle to harmonise the expectations of the peasants of Eastern Europe with the huge profits that have been accumulated by agri-businesses in Western Europe. Unless governments understand that land and tax policies are central to the fate of the EU, we are likely to see massive social upheavals that could end in violent conflicts. As the 10 new members are added to the Union in 2004, migration westwards can be expected on an unprecedented scale. The flow cannot be stemmed by disputes concerning notions of asylum. Most of the floating population will originate from the rural sectors.

Poland, for example, was a largely peasant country, but since the fall of Communism the family farms have become uneconomic. In a process reflecting the trends in Britain, some farmers are gobbling up the acres of adjoining farms, which in turn leaves more people without jobs – a polarisation of the population, with the concentration of land in fewer hands. This is creating the classic gap between the rich and poor. As one village council chairman, Jerzy Omielan, warned: "We cannot stop consolidation. But I am afraid this transformation is happening too fast. People must not be forced off the land too quickly because there are no alternative non-farm jobs".[5] Econ-

---

[5] Stefan Wagstyl, "Peasantries aside", *Financial Times Magazine*, 10 January 2004, p.27.

omists estimate that under present trends, rural unemployment could rise from about 18% (January 2004) to 30–45%. The landless of Poland, instead of sitting tight and suffering, will head south and west in search of jobs in Germany and Britain. When the leading economies in the EU slump into the next recession, unemployment will once again become the excuse for pathological reactions that will create tensions between member countries of the kind that were last observed, on a socially significant scale, during the rise of fascism in the years between the two world wars.

The folly of public policies has been concealed from public gaze by the failure to tabulate adequate data on the land market. In Britain, this information has been treated as a state secret – allegedly on the grounds that disclosure would be an infringement of people's rights. This is a curious argument when we remind ourselves of the vast quantity of private information that people have to disclose to the tax authorities. By law, we have to offer a complete profile of the way we earn our living by our labour. We have to disclose, down to the finest detail, our savings and assets. All this personal information, an intrusive state happily obliges us to reveal on pain of being fined or even imprisoned if we seek to preserve it as private. And yet, when it comes to the one asset over which the state claims the right to intrude (by way of eminent domain) in the public interest – land – we are told that disclosure must be avoided to protect the sensibilities of current owners.[6]

This concealment is driven by the fact that, historically, the land-owning aristocracy controlled Parliament and the public purse. As they methodically transferred the power of the Crown into their own hands, they were able to diminish the proportion of public revenue that was taken directly from the rent of land. Land rents are the natural revenue base for any community, but the aristocracy presumed to overturn this reality by creating new taxes which they placed on people's labour, savings and consumption. The graph on page 62 tracks the decline in the tax take

---

[6] Kevin Cahill, *Who Owns Britain: The Hidden Facts Behind Landownership in the UK and Ireland*, Edinburgh: Canongate Books, 2001.

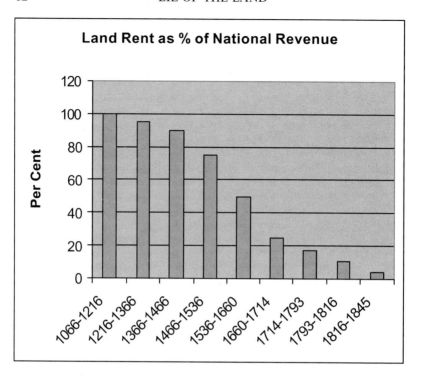

Land Rent as % of National Revenue

from land rents. The data are based on evidence presented to the House of Commons on 14th March 1842, by Richard Cobden, who championed the fight against the Corn Laws. This history is worth recalling, because it emphasises that the current disarray in rural policies has a tradition whose lessons have not yet been learnt.

The Corn Laws were presented as protection for farmers, but this perception was misleading. It is worth reading what one great historian wrote:[7]

> The protection of agriculture was hardly less important, but it was more difficult to find a solution likely to be accepted outside as well as inside parliament, because agricultural protection meant taxes on corn, and taxes on corn might well appear to be taxes imposed upon the community by

---

[7] Sir Llewellyn Woodward, *The Age of Reform, 1815–1870*, The Oxford History of England, 2nd edn., 1962, p.60.

Whig and Tory landlords acting in their own selfish interests. The country labourers gained nothing from the high price of bread, and the landlords represented no one save themselves and their tenant farmers. Thus after 1815 the attack upon the corn laws ... became an attack upon a comparatively small class accused of taking excessive profit from the ownership of land. The analysis of rent expounded by Ricardo and others added to the unpopularity of the landed interest.

The landowners held a majority in parliament, and the corn law of 1804 has been described as the first attempt by a parliament of landlords to legislate purely in their own interest as owners of arable soil, and to secure for themselves and their tenants the high prices resulting from war and bad harvests between 1793 and 1801.

The Anti-Corn Law League was founded in Manchester and London in 1839, following the formation of an anti-corn law association in Manchester in 1838. Woodward wrote:

> The support of Cobden and Bright was of immense value. These two men gave life and energy to the movement, and never allowed lack of immediate success to depress their public attitude ... Cobden took the view that aristocracies were naturally bellicose. 'The sooner the power in this country is transferred from the landed oligarchy, which has so misused it, and is placed absolutely – mind I say absolutely – in the hands of the intelligent middle and industrious classes, the better for the condition and destinies of this country'. The campaign against the corn laws was therefore part of a wider plan for the extension of free trade as an instrument of peace.[8]

When the Corn Laws were finally repealed on 25 June 1846, the Prime Minister, Sir Robert Peel, was defeated on another bill that same evening. He resigned on June 29. "His last speech as Prime Minister included a deliberate and magnificent eulogy of Cobden which offended Gladstone and Aberdeen because Cobden had argued for the repeal of the corn laws 'on the principle of holding up the landowners of England to the people as plunderers and knaves' ".[9]

---

[8] *Ibid.*, p. 120/121. Quoting *Cobden's Speeches*: ed J. Bright and Thorold Rogers, i 256. 15 Jan. 1845.
[9] Woodward, *op. cit.*, p. 124.

The lessons of that episode have not been learnt by Parliament, which now has an urgent duty to take control over the public finances and the way in which the Treasury raises public revenue. Parliament, to restore its credibility as an institution that represents the whole nation, needs to *undo* the harm it unleashed on the British public over several centuries, especially since 1660.

The return of Charles II, after the Cromwell experiment, ushered in a time when Parliament deliberately impoverished the people of Britain. That period continues to this day. Members of Parliament were landowners, as indeed were the voters. Parliament gained great power when it invited William of Orange to be King with Mary after the Glorious Revolution of 1688. It became even more powerful when Anne died and George I was invited to be King, a king of England who did not speak much English. Parliament had started its rise to supreme power and it made use of that power in the greediest manner.

The feudal lords had financed the government since 1066 when the vast majority of public revenue was raised from those privileged to be owners of land. Three quarters of public revenue was still being raised in that way by 1660. But Parliament now held sway, and Parliament was full of landowners, including the gentry and their circles of squires.

A gradual and consistent increase in taxes on the people was accompanied by a decrease in the revenue raised from land. When Richard Cobden, he of the Free Trade movement, spoke in 1842, only about 4% of revenue was coming from the land.[10] Cobden said:

> Thus the land, which anciently paid the whole of taxation, paid now only a fraction or one twenty-fifth, notwithstanding the immense increase that had taken place in the value of the rentals. The people had fared better under the despotic monarchs that when the powers of the state had fallen into the hands of a landed oligarchy, who had first exempted themselves from taxation, and next claimed compensation for themselves by a Corn Law for their heavy and peculiar burdens.

---

[10] Taken from Victor Saldji, 'New Light on Richard Cobden and the Land Question', paper presented to the Ninth International Conference on Land-Value Taxation and Free Trade, St. Andrews, Scotland, 15–20 August 1955.

Taxation on incomes, on earnings from savings and on the productive process burdens the economy with mind-boggling "deadweight losses".[11] Britain could increase its National Income by an enormous factor if Parliament were to insist that public revenue should once again be collected from the land.

Over the course of the 20th century, the great landlords lost their direct grip on Parliament. Instead, they were rescued by a perverse fiscal philosophy which prescribed a broad tax base – a tax net cast wide – which was sold to the public as the means to make taxation fairer. In fact, it was designed to conceal how much the government was taking off the people. Whether the tax is visible or not, it decreases the efficiency of the economy and lowers productivity.

In *Double-cross*, I stated that the National Audit Office (NAO) was barred from evaluating the policies employed by the Treasury. This would now seem to be incorrect. Following the publication of my study, Sir John Bourn KCB, Comptroller and Auditor General, replied that the NAO was "not barred from evaluating the value for money with which those policies are implemented. This includes the policies employed by the Treasury. To this extent there is no difference in our powers between spend and raise. On the suggestion that the NAO should be mandated to recommend a formula for the purpose of improving transparency and accountability with respect to the administration of the public's revenue, this must be for Parliament to decide".[12]

This was a reminder to Parliament that it has a duty to perform. Parliament can redeem itself, after centuries of deceiving the people over their public revenue, by instructing the NAO to estimate the deadweight losses that taxes foist onto the economy. The revelation that Britain was losing national income equivalent to as much as 80% of the nation's current output – the additional value that would be possible if the nation based its revenue on resource rents – would shock the electorate and concentrate the minds of MPs.

---

[11] The full figures are in Ronald Banks, *Double-cross – Gordon Brown, the Treasury & the hidden cost of taxes*, London: Centre for Land Policy Studies, London, 2001.

[12] Letter, 23 May 2002, in reference to *Double-cross*.

The second practical step is for Parliament to order a publicly-accessible database on land values. This would reverse a tradition of concealing the rental income of land. The absence of this information has impaired the ability of governments to employ policies that would boost the welfare of the population. It is an established fact, for example, that the one way to raise revenue without damaging people's incentives to work, save and invest, is to draw that revenue from the rent of land. One argument that has been used to oppose this policy is the claim that rent is insufficient as a revenue base to meet the expenses of the state. How can opponents of tax reform be so dogmatic when the evidence for their assertion does not exist in the official statistics?

And yet, when we know what to look for, we find that the fastest growing source of revenue is the rent of land. Australia, which is an exception to the general rule about the concealment of statistics, provides economists with the opportunity to measure those trends. One investigator analysed the national income over the 20th century.[13] The graph on page 67 summarises the data since 1972. It reveals what we would expect from theory. The rent attributable to land has increased faster than the revenue received by labour and capital.

With this information, it becomes possible to penetrate the veil of secrecy that shrouds agricultural policies in Britain. In the USA, commentators have no difficulty in tracing the link between taxpayer-funded subsidies and the beneficiaries with ease. But taxpayers are not the only losers. The discrimination is also felt by those who rent their farmland who, far from enjoying a subsidised windfall gain, "pay for it in the form of higher rent payments to landowners". Confirming the findings by Joel Dyer, Chuck Hassebrook, director of the Center for Rural Affairs in Walthill, Nebraska, said: "Farmers are sick and tired of having giant farms get federal subsidies to drive everybody else out of business".[14]

As Dr Pickard observes in his study, farmers are not just paying for the stresses that are now inflicted on them through

---

[13] Terry Dwyer, "The Taxable Capacity of Australian Land and Resources", *Australian Tax Forum*, Vol. 18(1), 2003.
[14] Laurent Belsie, "Farm subsidies prop up Midwest land values", *The Christian Science Monitor*, 4 January 2002.

Distribution of Real GDP: Australia

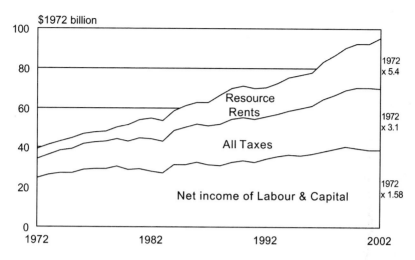

Source: Based on Terry Dwyer, 'The Taxable Capacity of Australian Land and Resources', Australian Tax Forum, Vol 18 No 1, 2003. Data for 2001-2002 extrapolated by Bryan Kavanagh, Land Values Research Group, Melbourne.

their bank balances; many of them are also paying with their lives. In the USA, suicide has become the No. 1 cause of death on the farms. Joel Dyer's investigation led him to an important conclusion that has yet to be adequately explored by social scientists:

> You don't just lose a farm. You lose your identity, your history, and, in many ways, your life.[15]

To reverse the tragic trends that originated with the displacement of people from the land, we first need an accurate portrait of the nation's income. Only then will it become possible for people to exercise their democratic right to know who gains from government policies. Under the current regime, the taxpayer is wilfully milked. The mechanism for this process of income redistribution is the land market. The veil of secrecy needs to be lifted, so that

[15] *Op. cit.*, p.3.

the financial implications of political decisions are transparent. Taxpayers can then decide how they want their public revenue distributed; and, most importantly, *how that revenue should be raised from them in the first place.* By terminating the abusive forms of taxation under which we currently labour, the collateral damage of land tenure and taxation – such as hunger, unemployment and territorial conflicts – may be ameliorated, if not abolished altogether.

LAND AND TAXATION
Nicolaus Tideman (ed)

Economic theory reveals that the optimum conditions for private enterprise exist when taxes on earned incomes from labour and capital are reduced to zero. Because modern economists insist on treating land as capital, they miss the obvious alternative, the unearned income from land. Prof. Mason Gaffney explains simply how land differs from capital and how failure to recognise this distorts the economy in many ways.

ISBN 0 85683 153 0 184pp **£14.95 pb**

LAND-VALUE TAXATION
The Equitable and Efficient Source of Public Finance
Kenneth Wenzer (ed)

'There is a sense in which all taxes are antagonistic to free enterprise – yet we need taxes . . . so which are the least harmful taxes? In my opinion, the least bad tax is the property tax on the unimproved value of land' MILTON FRIEDMAN

Twenty contributors endorse this view and examine the merits of land-value taxation.

ISBN 0 85683 182 4 320pp **£19.95 pb**

DYING FOR JUSTICE
George J. Miller MD

The link between ill health and poverty is well recognised. The Government's approach to the problem is in terms of funding, but, argues Prof Miller, one of Britain's leading medical scientists, government has to be funded out of taxation. As taxes reinforce the class structure and institutionalise poverty, this is self-defeating. The solution to the needlessly high cost of ill-health is to solve the problem of poverty, which requires a change in the way government raises its revenue.

ISBN 1 901202 04 6 80pp **£7.95 pb**

**For more information on similar books contact
Shepheard-Walwyn (Publishers) Ltd, Suite 604,
50 Westminster Bridge Road, London SE1 7QY
or visit the website: www.shepheard-walwyn.co.uk**